Key Stage Three
English
The Practice Tests

As you get towards the end of Key Stage 3, your school is likely to set you some tests to find out how you're doing in English.

Happily, this CGP book contains three complete sets of English practice tests so that you can go into the real thing fully prepared. We've even included detailed mark schemes so that you can mark your own work.

What CGP is all about

Our sole aim here at CGP is to produce the highest quality books — carefully written, immaculately presented and dangerously close to being funny.

Then we work our socks off to get them out to you — at the cheapest possible prices.

Published by CGP

Editors:
David Maliphant, Matteo Orsini Jones.

Contributors:
Elisabeth Sanderson, Nicola Woodfin.

With thanks to Hayley Thompson for the proofreading.
With thanks to Laura Jakubowski for the copyright research.

ISBN: 978 1 84762 175 7

Clipart from Corel®
Printed by Elanders Ltd, Newcastle upon Tyne

Contents

*The Reading Paper Pull-out is located at the back of this book.
You'll need it for the Reading Papers.*

How to Use This Book

This book contains loads of practice papers for Key Stage 3 English.

Understandably you're desperate to get started, but just hold your horses — there are **a few things you should know** first:

Here's What This Book Contains...

There are **three** sets of papers.
There are **mark schemes** for all the questions at the back of the book.
Use these to mark your work **after** you've had a go at the papers.

This is what's included in **each set** of papers:

Paper		Time Allowed	Marks Available
Reading Paper		15 minutes reading time, 1 hour writing time	32
Writing Paper	Section A	15 minutes planning time, 30 minutes writing time	30 (goes towards overall Writing score)
	Section B	30 minutes writing time	20 (goes towards overall Writing score)
Shakespeare Paper		45 minutes	18

Each **Reading Paper** has **three** bits of **writing** for you to read and answer questions on. These bits of writing are all in a **pull-out Reading Booklet** at the **back** of this book — so you've got easy access to them while you're answering the questions.

> Note: this book contains six Shakespeare Papers — three on scenes from <u>Romeo and Juliet</u> and three on scenes from <u>The Tempest</u>. The National Curriculum doesn't specify which Shakespeare plays you have to study at KS3, so these might not be the plays you're studying in class. It's best to check with your teacher if you're not sure.

To Get the Best Marks You Need to Keep Practising

1) These practice papers won't make you better at English, but they will show you what you **can** do, and what you **can't do**.

2) Do a test, **mark it** and look at where you went **wrong**. **That's** the stuff you need to **work on**.

3) **Go away**, **learn** those tricky bits, then **do the <u>same</u> test again**.
   If you're **still** going wrong, you'll have to do even **more practice** and **test yourself again**. Keep going until you get the **best possible marks**.

4) It doesn't sound like a lot of **fun**, but it really will **help**.

Six Top Tips for Doing Well

1) Read everything properly

The most important thing is to **understand** the questions.
Read everything **carefully** to be sure you're doing what they want.
In the **Reading paper**, if you don't read the passages properly you can't
possibly get good marks. You've got to pay attention to **every single word**.

2) Follow all the instructions

Some questions have special instructions.

In some questions you get a list of things to think about — include them **all**
in your answer. You'll get **more marks** if you do.

3) Look at the marks available

The **number of marks** you can get for a question gives you an idea of **how long** you
should spend on that question — spend **more time** on questions worth **more marks**.

4) Write your answers as clearly as you can

In a real exam, whoever's marking your paper won't be able to give you a mark if they
can't read your answer — even if it's right. You need to pay **special attention** to how
you write your answers in the Writing Papers:

- **Plan** your answer carefully for the longer task. You don't really have time for big
  mistakes, and it's **clear**, **well-organised** writing that gets the best marks.
- Be especially careful about your **punctuation** and **spelling**.
  There are marks put aside for spelling in the shorter writing question.

5) Check your work

Don't throw away easy marks — if you have any time at the end, make sure you go
back and read through your work to make sure you haven't made any silly mistakes.

6) Use spare paper

If you're going to do the practice papers more than once, write your
answers on a separate bit of paper.

Recording Your Progress

You can use the table below to keep a **record** of **how well you do** in each test. Don't forget to **look back** at what you got **wrong**, so you know what to **practise** for the **next test**.

Stick Your Marks in Here:

		Reading Paper (out of 32)	Writing Paper (out of 50)	Shakespeare Paper (out of 18)	Total Score (out of 100)
Set A	First go				
Set A	Second go				
Set A	Third go				
Set B	First go				
Set B	Second go				
Set B	Third go				
Set C	First go				
Set C	Second go				
Set C	Third go				

Levels

As of **September 2014**, there are no KS3 assessment levels. But you can use the table below to see what grades you'd have been likely to get under the **old levelling system**.

You'll need to use your **total score** for a paper set.

Mark	100-68	67-51	50-30	29-17	under 17
Level	7	6	5	4	N

Key Stage 3

English Test

Reading Paper
Vampires
Set A

English

KEY STAGE
3

PRACTICE PAPER
Reading
Set A

Reading Booklet
Set A

Vampires

English — Reading Booklet, Set A

Read this page, but don't open the booklet until your teacher says you can start. Write your name and school in the spaces below.

First Name _____

Last Name _____

School _____

Instructions

- Before you start to write, you have **15 minutes** to read the Reading Booklet.

- From that point you will have **1 hour** to write your answers.

- Try to answer **all** of the questions.

- There are **14** questions, worth **32 marks**.

- Check through all of your work carefully before the end of the test.

- If you're not sure what to do, ask your teacher.

Questions 1-5 are about *Yikes! Vampire Bats Can Run, Too*
(pages 3-4 in the Reading Booklet)

1. From the first paragraph of the article, write down three things a vampire bat can do.

    •................................   •................................   •................................

2. How does the title of the article grab the reader's attention? Explain one way.

    ....

    ....

3. Look at paragraphs 5 and 6. Explain one way in which the writer links these paragraphs together smoothly. Support your answer with a quotation.

    ....

    ....

    ....

4. a) From the first three paragraphs, write down a phrase which tells the reader that vampire bats can be quite fast.

    ....

    b) Write down a word from the section "On to the treadmill" which suggests that cattle move slowly.

    ....

5. In the whole article, how does the writer try to make the information entertaining and easy to understand for the reader?

You should comment on:
- the way the article is organised;
- the writer's use of informal language;
- the comparisons the writer uses.

....

....

....

....

....

....

....

....

....

....

....

....

....

....

5 marks

6. Look at paragraph 1. Give one way in which the writer makes the opening of the article interesting for a teenage audience.

....

1 mark

7. Give one reason from paragraph 4 why Darren Shan thinks that "Cirque Du Freak" is *not* a reckless or irresponsible book.

....

....

1 mark

8. In paragraph 5, what two elements does Darren Shan argue are needed for a good horror story?

....

....

....

2 marks

9. Explain how the whole article shows the author Darren Shan's enthusiasm for horror stories.

You should comment on:
- the language he uses to describe his own reactions to horror stories;
- the effects of the range of punctuation he uses;
- the way he writes about how a reader of horror stories should be affected.

....

....

....

....

....

....

....

....

....

....

....

....

....

....

5 marks

Questions 10-13 are about the extract from *Dracula* by Bram Stoker
(pages 7-8 in the Reading Booklet)

10. Give one detail in paragraph 1 that tells us that it is night-time.

....

1 mark

11. In the first 10 lines of paragraph 1, the narrator tells the reader how he feels about being in Count Dracula's castle. Pick out two phrases or sentences and explain what each one suggests about the narrator's feelings.
Write your answers in the table below.

Words from the text	What they suggest

2 marks

12. The narrator's feelings change between the middle of paragraph 1 and the middle of paragraph 2.

    a)   Describe the narrator's feelings in the middle of paragraph 1.
Support your answer with a quotation.

....

....

    b)   Describe the narrator's feelings by the middle of paragraph 2.
Support your answer with a quotation.

....

....

4 marks

13. In the last paragraph, the narrator repeats certain words. Pick out one example of repetition. Explain what it suggests to the reader about the narrator's state of mind.

Example

....

....

What it suggests about the narrator's state of mind

....

....

1 mark

14.   *Yikes! Vampire Bats Can Run Too* and *Dracula* each have a different tone and atmosphere. Complete the table below by explaining how each phrase makes the reader feel about the creature it is describing.

	Words from text	Effect on the reader
Yikes! Vampire Bats Can Run, Too	"Hopping is good, when you're a bat slurping cow blood, because cows are heavy and can kick or roll over and squash a bat"	
	"the clever little mammals dutifully kept pace"	
Dracula	"down the castle wall over the dreadful abyss, face down with his cloak spreading out around him like great wings."	
	"what manner of creature is it in the semblance of man?"	

4 marks

Key Stage 3

English Test

Writing Paper
Set A

English

KEY STAGE
3

PRACTICE PAPER
Writing
Set A

Read this page, but don't open the booklet until your teacher says you can start. Write your name and school in the spaces below.

First Name _____

Last Name _____

School _____

Instructions

■ This paper is **1 hour and 15 minutes** long.

■ You should spend about:

      45 minutes on Section A

      30 minutes on Section B

■ Section A, the longer writing task, is worth **30 marks**.

■ Section B, the shorter writing task, is worth **20 marks**.

■ You should spend 15 minutes planning your answer to Section A, using the planning grid provided.

■ Check through all of your work carefully before the end of the test.

■ If you're not sure what to do, ask your teacher.

Section A — Longer writing task

Improving the Common Room

Spend about 45 minutes on this section.

You are a member of your school's Student Council. Earlier in the year, the Council received some money from the Parents' Association to spend on improving the Year 9 common room. You get this note from the head of the Student Council:

> It's nearly the summer holidays, so I want to thank you for your help with the Student Council's work this year. I think we've achieved a lot!
>
> There's one last job to do before we enjoy that well earned rest. Do you remember that, earlier in the year, the Parents' Association gave us £100 to spend on the common room? Well, they're having a meeting soon and I need someone to write a formal report for them on how we spent the money. The report needs to explain what we've done, how it's improved things and what else still needs doing.
>
> Could you do this for me please?
> Thanks!

Write a report for the Parents' Association, explaining how the Student Council have spent the £100 on improving the Year 9 common room and what improvements are needed in the future.

(30 marks)

Use this page to plan your work.

This page will not be marked.

- Details of what you spent the money on and why

- How this has improved the facilities for Year 9 students

- What improvements are still needed in the common room and why

Section B — Shorter writing task

Summer Fair Fundraising

Spend about 30 minutes on this section.

You are helping to organise your school's summer fair. You receive this note from one of the other organisers:

Hi! How's it going?

I'm hoping we can raise over £1,000 this year — which would beat last year's target by £200. Since all profits go to charity, it's worth a try.

I'm having trouble getting enough volunteers for the stocks — you know, where you can pay to throw wet sponges at people. I've persuaded three Year 11 students to volunteer, but no teachers have yet.

Could you write a couple of paragraphs for the staff newsletter to try to persuade some of them to volunteer? You can keep it quite light-hearted. It would only be for ½ hour each, the sponges would be soaked in WARM water — and it is for charity!

Write a short article for the staff newsletter to persuade teachers to volunteer for a turn in the stocks at this year's summer fair.

(20 marks including 4 for spelling)

Key Stage 3

English Test

Shakespeare Paper
Romeo and Juliet
Set A

English

KEY STAGE
3

PRACTICE PAPER
Shakespeare
Set A

Read this page, but don't open the booklet until your teacher says you can start. Write your name and school in the spaces below.

First Name _____

Last Name _____

School _____

Instructions

- This test is **45 minutes** long.

- You will be tested on your reading and understanding of *Romeo and Juliet*. There are **18 marks** for this paper.

- Check through all of your work carefully before the end of the test.

- If you're not sure what to do, ask your teacher.

Romeo and Juliet
Act 1 Scene 1, lines 98 to 176
Act 2 Scene 2, lines 25 to 78

In the first extract, Montague wants to know why his servants
have been fighting, and why Romeo is so sad. In the second,
Romeo and Juliet talk about what is stopping them from
being together.

**What do you learn about different characters' attitudes to
love and family honour in these extracts?**

*Support your ideas by referring to both of the extracts which
are printed on the following pages.*

(18 marks)

Romeo and Juliet
Act 1 Scene 1, lines 98 to 176

In this extract, Montague asks Benvolio why his servants have been quarrelling. The Montagues also say that their son Romeo is sad. Benvolio decides to find out why.

All exit, except MONTAGUE, LADY MONTAGUE, *and* BENVOLIO.

MONTAGUE
Who set this ancient quarrel new abroach?
Speak, nephew, were you by when it began?

BENVOLIO
Here were the servants of your adversary, 100
And yours, close fighting ere I did approach:
I drew to part them — in the instant came
The fiery Tybalt, with his sword prepared,
Which, as he breathed defiance to my ears,
He swung about his head and cut the winds, 105
Who nothing hurt withal hissed him in scorn:
While we were interchanging thrusts and blows,
Came more and more and fought on part and part,
Till the Prince came, who parted either part.

LADY MONTAGUE
O, where is Romeo? Saw you him today? 110
Right glad I am he was not at this fray.

BENVOLIO
Madam, an hour before the worshipped sun
Peered forth the golden window of the east,
A troubled mind drove me to walk abroad,
Where, underneath the grove of sycamore 115
That westward rooteth from the city side,
So early walking did I see your son.
Towards him I made, but he was ware of me,
And stole into the covert of the wood:
I, measuring his affections by my own, 120
Which then most sought where most might not be found,
Being one too many by my weary self,
Pursued my humour, not pursuing his,
And gladly shunned who gladly fled from me.

MONTAGUE
Many a morning hath he there been seen, 125
With tears augmenting the fresh morning's dew.

Adding to clouds more clouds with his deep sighs;
But all so soon as the all-cheering sun
Should in the farthest east begin to draw
The shady curtains from Aurora's bed, 130
Away from light steals home my heavy son,
And private in his chamber pens himself,
Shuts up his windows, locks fair daylight out,
And makes himself an artificial night:
Black and portentous must this humour prove, 135
Unless good counsel may the cause remove.

BENVOLIO   My noble uncle, do you know the cause?

MONTAGUE   I neither know it, nor can learn of him.

BENVOLIO   Have you importuned him by any means?

MONTAGUE   Both by myself and many other friends: 140
But he, his own affections' counsellor,
Is to himself — I will not say how true —
But to himself so secret and so close,
So far from sounding and discovery,
As is the bud bit with an envious worm, 145
Ere he can spread his sweet leaves to the air,
Or dedicate his beauty to the sun.
Could we but learn from whence his sorrows grow.
We would as willingly give cure as know.

Enter ROMEO

BENVOLIO   See, where he comes. So please you, step aside; 150
I'll know his grievance, or be much denied.

MONTAGUE   I would thou wert so happy by thy stay,
To hear true shrift. Come, madam, let's away.

Exit MONTAGUE *and* LADY MONTAGUE

BENVOLIO   Good morrow, cousin.

ROMEO   Is the day so young?

BENVOLIO   But new struck nine.

ROMEO   Ay me! Sad hours seem long. 155
Was that my father that went hence so fast?

BENVOLIO   It was. What sadness lengthens Romeo's hours?

ROMEO	Not having that, which, having, makes them short.
BENVOLIO	In love?
ROMEO	Out —
BENVOLIO	Of love?
ROMEO	Out of her favour where I am in love.
BENVOLIO	Alas that love so gentle in his view, Should be so tyrannous and rough in proof!
ROMEO	Alas, that Love, whose view is muffled still, Should, without eyes, see pathways to his will! Where shall we dine? O me! What fray was here? Yet tell me not, for I have heard it all. Here's much to do with hate, but more with love. Why, then, O brawling love, O loving hate, O anything, of nothing first create! O heavy lightness, serious vanity, Misshapen chaos of well-seeming forms! Feather of lead, bright smoke, cold fire, sick health! Still-waking sleep, that is not what it is! This love feel I, that feel no love in this.

160

165

170

175

> In this extract, Romeo talks to Juliet at her balcony,
> and they both promise to give up their family names for love.

JULIET   Ay me!

ROMEO (*Aside*)   She speaks.   25
     O speak again, bright angel, for thou art
     As glorious to this night, being o'er my head,
     As is a wingèd messenger of heaven
     Unto the white-upturnèd wondering eyes
     Of mortals that fall back to gaze on him,   30
     When he bestrides the lazy-passing clouds,
     And sails upon the bosom of the air.

JULIET   O Romeo, Romeo, wherefore art thou Romeo?
     Deny thy father and refuse thy name.
     Or if thou wilt not, be but sworn my love,   35
     And I'll no longer be a Capulet.

ROMEO (*Aside*)   Shall I hear more, or shall I speak at this?

JULIET   'Tis but thy name that is my enemy —
     Thou art thyself, though not a Montague.
     What's Montague? It is nor hand nor foot,   40
     Nor arm nor face, nor any other part
     Belonging to a man. O be some other name!
     What's in a name? That which we call a rose
     By any other word would smell as sweet;
     So Romeo would, were he not Romeo called,   45
     Retain that dear perfection which he owes
     Without that title. Romeo, doff thy name,
     And for thy name, which is no part of thee,
     Take all myself.

ROMEO   I take thee at thy word.
     Call me but love, and I'll be new baptised;   50
     Henceforth I never will be Romeo.

JULIET   What man art thou that thus bescreened in night
     So stumblest on my counsel?

ROMEO   By a name
     I know not how to tell thee who I am.
     My name, dear saint, is hateful to myself,   55
     Because it is an enemy to thee;
     Had I it written, I would tear the word.

JULIET	My ears have yet not drunk a hundred words	
	Of thy tongue's uttering, yet I know the sound.	
	Art thou not Romeo, and a Montague?	60
ROMEO	Neither, fair maid, if either thee dislike.	
JULIET	How camest thou hither, tell me, and wherefore?	
	The orchard walls are high and hard to climb,	
	And the place death, considering who thou art,	
	If any of my kinsmen find thee here.	65
ROMEO	With love's light wings did I o'erperch these walls,	
	For stony limits cannot hold love out,	
	And what love can do, that dares love attempt:	
	Therefore thy kinsmen are no stop to me.	
JULIET	If they do see thee, they will murder thee.	70
ROMEO	Alack, there lies more peril in thine eye	
	Than twenty of their swords. Look thou but sweet,	
	And I am proof against their enmity.	
JULIET	I would not for the world they saw thee here.	
ROMEO	I have night's cloak to hide me from their eyes,	75
	And but thou love me, let them find me here.	
	My life were better ended by their hate,	
	Than death prorogued, wanting of thy love.	

END OF TEST

Key Stage 3

English Test

Shakespeare Paper
The Tempest

Set A

Read this page, but don't open the booklet until your teacher says you can start. Write your name and school in the spaces below.

First Name _____

Last Name _____

School _____

Instructions

- This test is **45 minutes** long.

- You will be tested on your reading and understanding of *The Tempest*. There are **18 marks** for this paper.

- Check through all of your work carefully before the end of the test.

- If you're not sure what to do, ask your teacher.

The Tempest
Act 1 Scene 2, lines 390 to 453
Act 3 Scene 1, lines 37 to 91

In the first extract, Ferdinand has just been shipwrecked
and is led away by Ariel to meet Miranda. In the second,
Ferdinand and Miranda promise to marry each other.

**In these extracts, how does Ferdinand's language show
how he is feeling?**

*Support your ideas by referring to both of the extracts which
are printed on the following pages.*

(18 marks)

The Tempest
Act 1 Scene 2, lines 390 to 453

> In this extract, Ferdinand meets Miranda for the first time and instantly falls in love with her.
> He wants to impress her but he is still sad about the death of his father.

FERDINAND	Where should this music be? I' th' air or th' earth?	390
	It sounds no more, and sure it waits upon	
	Some god o' th' island. Sitting on a bank,	
	Weeping again the King my father's wreck,	
	This music crept by me upon the waters,	
	Allaying both their fury and my passion	395
	With its sweet air. Thence I have followed it,	
	Or it hath drawn me rather. But 'tis gone.	
	No, it begins again.	
ARIEL (*Sings*)	Full fathom five thy father lies;	
	Of his bones are coral made;	400
	Those are pearls that were his eyes;	
	Nothing of him that doth fade	
	But doth suffer a sea-change	
	Into something rich and strange.	
	Sea-nymphs hourly ring his knell:	405
SPIRITS	Ding-dong.	
ARIEL	Hark! Now I hear them.	
ARIEL and SPIRITS	Ding dong bell.	
FERDINAND	The ditty does remember my drowned father.	
	This is no mortal business, nor no sound	410
	That the earth owes. I hear it now above me.	
PROSPERO (*To* MIRANDA)	The fringed curtains of thine eye advance,	
	And say what thou seest yond.	
MIRANDA	What is't? A spirit?	
	Lord, how it looks about! Believe me, sir,	
	It carries a brave form. But 'tis a spirit.	415
PROSPERO	No, wench — it eats and sleeps and hath such senses	
	As we have, such. This gallant which thou seest	
	Was in the wreck, and but he's something stained	
	With grief, that's beauty's canker, thou mightst call him	
	A goodly person. He hath lost his fellows,	420
	And strays about to find 'em.	
MIRANDA	I might call him	
	A thing divine, for nothing natural	
	I ever saw so noble.	

PROSPERO (*Aside*)   It goes on, I see,
                    As my soul prompts it. Spirit, fine spirit! I'll free thee
                    Within two days for this.

FERDINAND (*Seeing* MIRANDA)   Most sure, the goddess   425
                    On whom these airs attend! Vouchsafe my pray'r
                    May know if you remain upon this island,
                    And that you will some good instruction give
                    How I may bear me here. My prime request,
                    Which I do last pronounce, is — O you wonder! —   430
                    If you be maid or no?

MIRANDA   No wonder, sir —
                    But certainly a maid.

FERDINAND   My language? Heavens!
                    I am the best of them that speak this speech,
                    Were I but where 'tis spoken.

PROSPERO   How the best?
                    What wert thou, if the King of Naples heard thee?   435

FERDINAND   A single thing, as I am now, that wonders
                    To hear thee speak of Naples. He does hear me,
                    And that he does I weep. Myself am Naples,
                    Who with mine eyes, never since at ebb, beheld
                    The King my father wrecked.

MIRANDA   Alack, for mercy!   440

FERDINAND   Yes, faith, and all his lords, the Duke of Milan
                    And his brave son being twain.

PROSPERO (*Aside*)   The Duke of Milan
                    And his more braver daughter could control thee,
                    If now 'twere fit to do't. At the first sight
                    They have changed eyes. Delicate Ariel,   445
                    I'll set thee free for this. (*To* FERDINAND) A word,
                                        good sir —
                    I fear you have done yourself some wrong — a word.

MIRANDA (*Aside*)   Why speaks my father so ungently? This
                    Is the third man that e'er I saw, the first
                    That e'er I sighed for. Pity move my father   450
                    To be inclined my way!

FERDINAND   O, if a virgin,
                    And your affection not gone forth, I'll make you
                    The Queen of Naples.

In this extract, Ferdinand works hard to complete the task
Prospero has set him. He talks to Miranda about his feelings for
her and they promise to get married.

FERDINAND   Admired Miranda!
Indeed the top of admiration, worth
What's dearest to the world! Full many a lady
I have eyed with best regard, and many a time   40
Th' harmony of their tongues hath into bondage
Brought my too diligent ear. For several virtues
Have I liked several women, never any
With so full soul, but some defect in her
Did quarrel with the noblest grace she owed,   45
And put it to the foil — but you, O you,
So perfect and so peerless, are created
Of every creature's best!

MIRANDA   I do not know
One of my sex, no woman's face remember,
Save, from my glass, mine own, nor have I seen   50
More that I may call men than you, good friend,
And my dear father. How features are abroad,
I am skilless of, but, by my modesty,
The jewel in my dower, I would not wish
Any companion in the world but you,   55
Nor can imagination form a shape,
Besides yourself, to like of. But I prattle
Something too wildly, and my father's precepts
I therein do forget.

FERDINAND   I am, in my condition,
A prince, Miranda. I do think, a king —   60
I would not so — and would no more endure
This wooden slavery than to suffer
The flesh-fly blow my mouth! Hear my soul speak:
The very instant that I saw you, did
My heart fly to your service, there resides   65
To make me slave to it, and for your sake
Am I this patient log-man.

MIRANDA	Do you love me?

FERDINAND O heaven, O earth, bear witness to this sound,
And crown what I profess with kind event,
If I speak true! If hollowly, invert   70
What best is boded me to mischief! I,
Beyond all limit of what else i' th' world,
Do love, prize, honour you.

MIRANDA   I am a fool
To weep at what I am glad of.

PROSPERO (*Aside*)   Fair encounter
Of two most rare affections! Heavens rain grace   75
On that which breeds between 'em!

FERDINAND   Wherefore weep you?

MIRANDA At mine unworthiness, that dare not offer
What I desire to give, and much less take
What I shall die to want. But this is trifling,
And all the more it seeks to hide itself,   80
The bigger bulk it shows. Hence, bashful cunning,
And prompt me, plain and holy innocence!
I am your wife, if you will marry me,
If not, I'll die your maid. To be your fellow
You may deny me, but I'll be your servant,   85
Whether you will or no.

FERDINAND (*He kneels*)   My mistress, dearest,
And I thus humble ever.

MIRANDA   My husband, then?

FERDINAND Ay, with a heart as willing
As bondage e'er of freedom. Here's my hand.

MIRANDA And mine, with my heart in't. And now farewell   90
Till half an hour hence.

FERDINAND   A thousand thousand!

END OF TEST

Key Stage 3

English Test

Reading Paper
Changing Schools
Set B

Set B

**Changing
Schools**

Read this page, but don't open the booklet until your teacher says you can start. Write your name and school in the spaces below.

First Name _____

Last Name _____

School _____

Instructions

- Before you start to write, you have **15 minutes** to read the Reading Booklet.

- From that point you will have **1 hour** to write your answers.

- Try to answer **all** of the questions.

- There are **13** questions, worth **32 marks**.

- Check through all of your work carefully before the end of the test.

- If you're not sure what to do, ask your teacher.

1. From the first paragraph, write down why it was difficult for Harry to remember
    where things were in his new school.

    ....

    ....

    1 mark

2. a) In paragraph 2, the writer lists the ways that Peeves is unpleasant.
        Write down one phrase that shows he is unpleasant.

        ....

        1 mark

    b) Explain why the list of ways Peeves is unpleasant is an effective way of
        describing his personality to the reader.

        ....

        ....

        1 mark

3. The writer uses humour in her descriptions of the school.
    Give one example of humour and explain why it is effective.

    Example from text

    ....

    Why it is effective

    ....

    2 marks

4. In the whole text, how does the writer create a magical atmosphere for Hogwarts School?

You should comment on:
- the language the writer uses;
- the unusual features of the school building and lessons;
- the descriptions of characters.

....

....

....

....

....

....

....

....

....

....

....

....

....

5 marks

5. Describe one technique the writer uses to attract the reader's attention in paragraph 1. Explain why it is effective.

....

....

....

2 marks

6. From Chenice's account, give one impression you get of the school. Support your answer with a quotation.

....

....

....

2 marks

7. Complete the table below to show how the way the article is organised makes it more useful to the reader.

How the article is organised	How this helps the reader
General introduction to changing schools	Helps the reader to understand what the students are going to talk about
Sections describing different pupils' experiences	
Headline and subheadings	

2 marks

8. What impression does the article give about what it's like to start secondary school?

You should comment on:
- the feelings described by the children;
- the language used in the introduction;
- the headmaster's comment.

....

....

....

....

....

....

....

....

....

....

....

....

....

....

5 marks

9. From paragraphs 1 and 2 what overall impression do you get of the evacuees' experience? Give one quotation to support your answer.

....

....

....

2 marks

10. How do the logbook extracts suggest that the school is old-fashioned compared to today's schools? Give one example.

....

1 mark

11. Why do you think the extracts from the logbook are included in the article? Suggest one reason.

....

....

1 mark

12. Pick out three phrases from paragraph 3 that show that the school was uncomfortable for the children. Explain the effect of these phrases on the reader.

Phrase 1

....

....

Effect on Reader

....

....

Phrase 2

....

....

Effect on Reader

....

....

Phrase 3

....

....

Effect on Reader

....

....

3 marks

13. Both *Wingrave School* and *Harry Potter and the Philosopher's Stone* describe characters adapting to unusual conditions at school. However, they are very different types of text.

Complete the table below by:

• Circling what you think the purpose of each text is.

• Explaining your choices.

	Wingrave School	***Harry Potter and the Philosopher's Stone***
Purpose of the text (circle your answer)	entertaining informing persuading	entertaining informing persuading
Give a reason for your choice		

4 marks

English

KEY STAGE 3

PRACTICE PAPER
Writing
Set B

Key Stage 3

English Test

Writing Paper
Set B

Read this page, but don't open the booklet until your teacher says you can start. Write your name and school in the spaces below.

First Name _____

Last Name _____

School _____

Instructions

- This paper is **1 hour and 15 minutes** long.

- You should spend about:

     45 minutes on Section A

     30 minutes on Section B

- Section A, the longer writing task, is worth **30 marks**.

- Section B, the shorter writing task, is worth **20 marks**.

- You should spend 15 minutes planning your answer to Section A, using the planning grid provided.

- Check through all of your work carefully before the end of the test.

- If you're not sure what to do, ask your teacher.

Section A — Longer writing task

Teen Readers

Spend about 45 minutes on this section.

You have a Saturday job at the local library.

Your boss gives you this information:

I would like to encourage more teenagers to use the library. Maybe we need to make the teenage book section more attractive. Or we could offer more services to teenagers — libraries are about more than books. Other libraries in the area are offering:

- free internet access for school pupils
- homework clubs

Please write a report advising me about why teenagers don't like using the library at the moment and what we could do to encourage them to use the library more.

Write a report to advise your boss about why teenagers aren't using the library now, and how you think more teenagers could be encouraged to use the library in the future.

(30 marks)

Use this page to plan your work.

This page will not be marked.

> · Why don't teenagers like the library at the moment?

> · What could the library do to attract more teenagers?

> · Why would these things attract teenagers?

Section B — Shorter writing task

Talent Contest

Spend about 30 minutes on this section.

You have volunteered to help organise the school's talent contest.
The teacher in charge gives you this note:

> Pupils entering the contest need to know what they're letting themselves in for!
>
> They need to know how long they have to perform for and the sorts of things they could do.
>
> They also need to know what time it's on, where it's being held and what they need to bring with them.

Write a leaflet informing pupils about the details of the talent contest.

(20 marks including 4 for spelling)

Key Stage 3

English Test

Shakespeare Paper
Romeo and Juliet

Set B

Read this page, but don't open the booklet until your teacher says you can start. Write your name and school in the spaces below.

First Name _____

Last Name _____

School _____

Instructions

- This test is **45 minutes** long.

- You will be tested on your reading and understanding of *Romeo and Juliet*. There are **18 marks** for this paper.

- Check through all of your work carefully before the end of the test.

- If you're not sure what to do, ask your teacher.

Romeo and Juliet

Act 1 Scene 1, lines 154 to 218
Act 2 Scene 2, lines 79 to 135

In the first extract Romeo tells Benvolio about Rosaline, a girl he loves. In the second, Romeo and Juliet say that they love each other.

How does Shakespeare use language to show strong emotions in these extracts?

Support your ideas by referring to both of the extracts which are printed on the following pages.

(18 marks)

Romeo and Juliet
Act 1 Scene 1, lines 154 to 218

In this extract, Romeo tells Benvolio about Rosaline, a girl he is in love with.

Exit MONTAGUE *and* LADY MONTAGUE

BENVOLIO	Good morrow, cousin.	
ROMEO	Is the day so young?	
BENVOLIO	But new struck nine.	
ROMEO	Ay me! Sad hours seem long.	155
	Was that my father that went hence so fast?	
BENVOLIO	It was. What sadness lengthens Romeo's hours?	
ROMEO	Not having that, which, having, makes them short.	
BENVOLIO	In love?	
ROMEO	Out —	160
BENVOLIO	Of love?	
ROMEO	Out of her favour where I am in love.	
BENVOLIO	Alas that love so gentle in his view,	
	Should be so tyrannous and rough in proof!	
ROMEO	Alas, that Love, whose view is muffled still,	165
	Should, without eyes, see pathways to his will!	
	Where shall we dine? O me! What fray was here?	
	Yet tell me not, for I have heard it all.	
	Here's much to do with hate, but more with love.	
	Why, then, O brawling love, O loving hate,	170
	O anything, of nothing first create!	
	O heavy lightness, serious vanity,	
	Misshapen chaos of well-seeming forms!	
	Feather of lead, bright smoke, cold fire, sick health!	
	Still-waking sleep, that is not what it is!	175
	This love feel I, that feel no love in this.	
	Dost thou not laugh?	
BENVOLIO	No, coz, I rather weep.	
ROMEO	Good heart, at what?	
BENVOLIO	At thy good heart's oppression.	
ROMEO	Why, such is love's transgression.	
	Griefs of mine own lie heavy in my breast,	180
	Which thou wilt propagate, to have it pressed	

With more of thine; this love that thou hast shown
Doth add more grief to too much of mine own.
Love is a smoke made with the fume of sighs,
Being purged, a fire sparkling in lovers' eyes,   185
Being vexed a sea nourished with lovers' tears:
What is it else? A madness most discreet,
A choking gall and a preserving sweet.
Farewell, my coz.

BENVOLIO   Soft! I will go along;
And if you leave me so, you do me wrong.   190

ROMEO   Tut, I have lost myself; I am not here,
This is not Romeo, he's some other where.

BENVOLIO   Tell me in sadness, who is that you love.

ROMEO   What, shall I groan and tell thee?

BENVOLIO   Groan! Why no,
But sadly tell me, who?   195

ROMEO   Bid a sick man in sadness make his will?
Ah, word ill urged to one that is so ill.
In sadness, cousin, I do love a woman.

BENVOLIO   I aimed so near, when I supposed you loved.

ROMEO   A right good mark-man! And she's fair I love.   200

BENVOLIO   A right fair mark, fair coz, is soonest hit.

ROMEO   Well, in that hit you miss: she'll not be hit
With Cupid's arrow, she hath Dian's wit;
And, in strong proof of chastity well armed,
From love's weak childish bow she lives uncharmed.   205
She will not stay the siege of loving terms,
Nor bide th'encounter of assailing eyes,
Nor ope her lap to saint-seducing gold:
O, she is rich in beauty, only poor,
That when she dies with beauty dies her store.   210

BENVOLIO   Then she hath sworn that she will still live chaste?

ROMEO   She hath, and in that sparing makes huge waste,
For beauty starved with her severity
Cuts beauty off from all posterity.
She is too fair, too wise, wisely too fair,   215
To merit bliss by making me despair:
She hath forsworn to love, and in that vow
Do I live dead that live to tell it now.

Act 2 Scene 2, lines 79 to 135

In this extract, Juliet talks to Romeo from her balcony.

JULIET	By whose direction found'st thou out this place?	
ROMEO	By Love, that first did prompt me to enquire:	80
	He lent me counsel, and I lent him eyes.	
	I am no pilot, yet wert thou as far	
	As that vast shore washed with the farthest sea,	
	I should adventure for such merchandise.	
JULIET	Thou knowest the mask of night is on my face,	85
	Else would a maiden blush bepaint my cheek	
	For that which thou hast heard me speak tonight.	
	Fain would I dwell on form, fain, fain deny	
	What I have spoke, but farewell compliment.	
	Dost thou love me? I know thou wilt say 'Ay',	90
	And I will take thy word; yet if thou swear'st,	
	Thou mayst prove false: at lovers' perjuries	
	They say Jove laughs. O gentle Romeo,	
	If thou dost love, pronounce it faithfully.	
	Or if thou think'st I am too quickly won,	95
	I'll frown and be perverse, and say thee nay,	
	So thou wilt woo, but else not for the world.	
	In truth, fair Montague, I am too fond,	
	And therefore thou mayst think my behaviour light:	
	But trust me, gentleman, I'll prove more true	100
	Than those that have more cunning to be strange.	
	I should have been more strange, I must confess,	
	But that thou overheard'st, ere I was ware,	
	My true-love passion — therefore pardon me,	
	And not impute this yielding to light love,	105
	Which the dark night hath so discoverèd.	
ROMEO	Lady, by yonder blessèd moon I vow,	
	That tips with silver all these fruit-tree tops —	
JULIET	O swear not by the moon, th'inconstant moon,	
	That monthly changes in her circled orb,	110
	Lest that thy love prove likewise variable.	

ROMEO	What shall I swear by?	
JULIET	Do not swear at all.	
	Or if thou wilt, swear by thy gracious self,	
	Which is the god of my idolatry,	
	And I'll believe thee.	
ROMEO	If my heart's dear love —	115
JULIET	Well, do not swear. Although I joy in thee,	
	I have no joy of this contract tonight,	
	It is too rash, too unadvised, too sudden,	
	Too like the lightning, which doth cease to be	
	Ere one can say 'It lightens'. Sweet, good night.	120
	This bud of love, by summer's ripening breath,	
	May prove a beauteous flower when next we meet.	
	Good night, good night! as sweet repose and rest	
	Come to thy heart as that within my breast.	
ROMEO	O wilt thou leave me so unsatisfied?	125
JULIET	What satisfaction canst thou have tonight?	
ROMEO	Th'exchange of thy love's faithful vow for mine.	
JULIET	I gave thee mine before thou didst request it,	
	And yet I would it were to give again.	
ROMEO	Wouldst thou withdraw it? For what purpose, love?	130
JULIET	But to be frank and give it thee again,	
	And yet I wish but for the thing I have.	
	My bounty is as boundless as the sea,	
	My love as deep; the more I give to thee	
	The more I have, for both are infinite.	135

The NURSE calls to JULIET from inside the house.

END OF TEST

English
KEY STAGE 3
PRACTICE PAPER
Shakespeare
Set B

Key Stage 3

English Test

Shakespeare Paper
The Tempest
Set B

Read this page, but don't open the booklet until your teacher says you can start. Write your name and school in the spaces below.

First Name _____

Last Name _____

School _____

Instructions

- This test is **45 minutes** long.

- You will be tested on your reading and understanding of *The Tempest*. There are **18 marks** for this paper.

- Check through all of your work carefully before the end of the test.

- If you're not sure what to do, ask your teacher.

The Tempest
Act 1 Scene 2, lines 421 to 479
Act 3 Scene 1, lines 1 to 59

In the first extract, Miranda falls in love with Ferdinand and begs her father to be kind to him; in the second Miranda begs Ferdinand to stop working and offers to help.

What do you learn about Miranda's character from her language and actions in these extracts?

Support your ideas by referring to both of the extracts which are printed on the following pages.

(18 marks)

The Tempest
Act 1 Scene 2, lines 421 to 479

> In this extract, Miranda meets Ferdinand for the first time and the couple begin to fall in love. She tries to protect Ferdinand from her father who wants to test him.

MIRANDA

                               I might call him
A thing divine, for nothing natural
I ever saw so noble.

PROSPERO (*Aside*)

                        It goes on, I see,
As my soul prompts it. (*To* ARIEL) Spirit, fine spirit!
                    I'll free thee
Within two days for this.

FERDINAND

           (*Seeing* MIRANDA) Most sure, the goddess   425
On whom these airs attend! Vouchsafe my pray'r
May know if you remain upon this island,
And that you will some good instruction give
How I may bear me here. My prime request,
Which I do last pronounce, is — O you wonder! —   430
If you be maid or no?

MIRANDA

                  No wonder, sir —
But certainly a maid.

FERDINAND

              My language? Heavens!
I am the best of them that speak this speech,
Were I but where 'tis spoken.

PROSPERO

                How the best?
What wert thou, if the King of Naples heard thee?   435

FERDINAND

A single thing, as I am now, that wonders
To hear thee speak of Naples. He does hear me,
And that he does I weep. Myself am Naples,
Who with mine eyes, never since at ebb, beheld
The King my father wrecked.

MIRANDA

                  Alack, for mercy!   440

FERDINAND

Yes, faith, and all his lords, the Duke of Milan
And his brave son being twain.

PROSPERO (*Aside*)

                  The Duke of Milan
And his more braver daughter could control thee,
If now 'twere fit to do't. At the first sight
They have changed eyes. Delicate Ariel,   445

	I'll set thee free for this. (*To* FERDINAND) A word, good sir —	
	I fear you have done yourself some wrong — a word.	
MIRANDA (*Aside*)	Why speaks my father so ungently? This	
	Is the third man that e'er I saw, the first	
	That e'er I sighed for. Pity move my father	450
	To be inclined my way!	
FERDINAND	O, if a virgin,	
	And your affection not gone forth, I'll make you	
	The Queen of Naples.	
PROSPERO	Soft, sir, one word more!	
	(*Aside*) They are both in either's pow'rs, but this swift business	
	I must uneasy make, lest too light winning	455
	Make the prize light. (*To* FERDINAND) One word more —	
	I charge thee	
	That thou attend me — thou dost here usurp	
	The name thou ow'st not and hast put thyself	
	Upon this island as a spy, to win it	
	From me, the lord on't.	
FERDINAND	No, as I am a man.	460
MIRANDA	There's nothing ill can dwell in such a temple.	
	If the ill spirit have so fair a house,	
	Good things will strive to dwell with't.	
PROSPERO	(*To* FERDINAND) Follow me.	
	(*To* MIRANDA) Speak not you for him — he's a traitor.	
	(*To* FERDINAND) Come!	
	I'll manacle thy neck and feet together.	465
	Sea-water shalt thou drink, thy food shall be	
	The fresh-brook mussels, withered roots, and husks	
	Wherein the acorn cradled. Follow.	
FERDINAND	No —	
	I will resist such entertainment till	
	Mine enemy has more power.	

He draws his sword, and is charmed from moving.

MIRANDA	O dear father!	470
	Make not too rash a trial of him, for	
	He's gentle, and not fearful.	

PROSPERO

                                        What, I say,
                My foot my tutor? *(To* FERDINAND*)* Put thy sword up, traitor,
                Who mak'st a show but dar'st not strike, thy conscience
                Is so possessed with guilt. Come from thy ward,   475
                For I can here disarm thee with this stick
                And make thy weapon drop.

MIRANDA

                                        Beseech you, father!

PROSPERO   Hence! Hang not on my garments.

MIRANDA

                                                Sir, have pity.
                I'll be his surety.

Act 3 Scene 1, lines 1 to 59

> In this extract, in order to prove his love for Miranda, Ferdinand
> works hard to complete the task Prospero has set him. Miranda
> begs Ferdinand to stop work and offers to help him.

In front of PROSPERO*'s cave.*

Enter FERDINAND*, bearing a log*

FERDINAND   There be some sports are painful, and their labour
                Delight in them sets off, some kinds of baseness
                Are nobly undergone, and most poor matters
                Point to rich ends. This my mean task
                Would be as heavy to me as odious, but   5
                The mistress which I serve quickens what's dead,
                And makes my labours pleasures. O, she is
                Ten times more gentle than her father's crabbed,
                And he's composed of harshness. I must remove
                Some thousands of these logs, and pile them up,   10
                Upon a sore injunction. My sweet mistress
                Weeps when she sees me work, and says such baseness
                Had never like executor. I forget —
                But these sweet thoughts do even refresh my labours
                Most busiest when I do it.

Enter MIRANDA*, and* PROSPERO *at a distance, unseen*

MIRANDA   Alas, now, pray you,   15
Work not so hard. I would the lightning had
Burnt up those logs that you are enjoined to pile.
Pray, set it down and rest you. When this burns,
'Twill weep for having wearied you. My father
Is hard at study. Pray, now, rest yourself.   20
He's safe for these three hours.

FERDINAND   O most dear mistress,
The sun will set before I shall discharge
What I must strive to do.

MIRANDA   If you'll sit down,
I'll bear your logs the while. Pray give me that,
I'll carry it to the pile.

FERDINAND   No, precious creature —   25
I had rather crack my sinews, break my back,
Than you should such dishonour undergo,
While I sit lazy by.

MIRANDA   It would become me
As well as it does you, and I should do it
With much more ease, for my good will is to it,   30
And yours it is against.

PROSPERO (Aside)   Poor worm, thou art infected!
This visitation shows it.

MIRANDA   You look wearily.

FERDINAND   No, noble mistress — 'tis fresh morning with me
When you are by at night. I do beseech you,
Chiefly that I might set it in my prayers,   35
What is your name?

MIRANDA   Miranda — O my father,
I have broke your hest to say so!

FERDINAND   Admired Miranda!
Indeed the top of admiration, worth
What's dearest to the world! Full many a lady
I have eyed with best regard, and many a time   40
Th' harmony of their tongues hath into bondage
Brought my too diligent ear. For several virtues
Have I liked several women, never any

With so full soul, but some defect in her
Did quarrel with the noblest grace she owed,   45
And put it to the foil — but you, O you,
So perfect and so peerless, are created
Of every creature's best!

MIRANDA   I do not know
One of my sex, no woman's face remember,
Save, from my glass, mine own, nor have I seen   50
More that I may call men than you, good friend,
And my dear father. How features are abroad,
I am skilless of, but, by my modesty,
The jewel in my dower, I would not wish
Any companion in the world but you,   55
Nor can imagination form a shape,
Besides yourself, to like of. But I prattle
Something too wildly, and my father's precepts
I therein do forget.

END OF TEST

Key Stage 3

English Test

Reading Paper
The Great Outdoors
Set C

Set C

The Great
Outdoors

Read this page, but don't open the booklet until your teacher says you can start. Write your name and school in the spaces below.

First Name _____

Last Name _____

School _____

Instructions

■ Before you start to write, you have **15 minutes** to read the Reading Booklet.

■ From that point you will have **1 hour** to write your answers.

■ Try to answer **all** of the questions.

■ There are **14** questions, worth **32 marks**.

■ Check through all of your work carefully before the end of the test.

■ If you're not sure what to do, ask your teacher.

1. Write down a phrase from the first three verses describing the freedom and solitude the poet finds in the bush.

    ....

    1 mark

2. Write down two similes from the last verse.

    ....

    ....

    2 marks

3. The writer repeats a phrase in the first three verses.

    a) Write down the repeated phrase.

        ....

        1 mark

    b) What effect do you think the repetition of this phrase has on the reader?

        ....

        ....

        1 mark

4. In the whole poem, how does the writer create a picture of the bush?
You should write about:
- descriptions of landscape;
- descriptions of plants and trees;
- the poet's attitude to the bush.

....

....

....

....

....

....

....

....

....

....

....

....

....

....

5 marks

5. Write down one phrase from lines 1-5 that tells us that this is an important day for the narrator.

....

1 mark

6. Write down two phrases from lines 39-49 describing the scenery.

....

....

1 mark

7. Describe three ways in which the writer builds the feelings of tension between lines 50 and 58.

Support your answer with quotations.

....

....

....

....

....

....

....

3 marks

8. From lines 6-13 and 60-67, pick out four pieces of information about the techniques involved in climbing and looking after climbing equipment.

1	
2	
3	
4	

2 marks

9. Using the whole extract, explain how the writer helps the reader to understand her feelings as she sets out on the climb.

You should comment on:
- how the writer mixes information and description;
- how her language brings the scene to life;
- how successful you think she is at making the reader feel involved in the description of her experiences.

....

....

....

....

....

....

....

....

....

....

....

....

....

5 marks

10. From paragraph 1, pick out two words or phrases that show this magazine is written in a style designed to appeal to young people.

....

1 mark

11. From Andrew's answers in the interview, choose two statements that show he is committed to his sport. Explain your choices.

....

....

....

....

2 marks

12. From paragraphs 2 to 9 (the interview), find two quotations that suggest what Andrew is like as a person and explain what they tell you.

Quotation	What it tells you about Andrew's personality
1.	
2.	

2 marks

13. Using paragraph 9, explain why Andrew's parents decided to buy him a mountain bike.

....

1 mark

Question 14 is about *two of the texts*

14. This question is about *Going Up* **and** *Mountain Bike Champion.*
It asks you to compare the two texts.

Write down one similarity between *Going Up* and *Mountain Bike Champion:*

....

Describe how this feature of the texts affects the reader:

....

....

Write down one difference between *Going Up* and *Mountain Bike Champion*:

....

Describe how this difference between the texts affects the reader:

....

....

4 marks

Key Stage 3

English Test

Writing Paper
Set C

Read this page, but don't open the booklet until your teacher says you can start. Write your name and school in the spaces below.

First Name _____

Last Name _____

School _____

Instructions

- This paper is **1 hour and 15 minutes** long.

- You should spend about:

    45 minutes on Section A

    30 minutes on Section B

- Section A, the longer writing task, is worth **30 marks**.

- Section B, the shorter writing task, is worth **20 marks**.

- You should spend 15 minutes planning your answer to Section A, using the planning grid provided.

- Check through all of your work carefully before the end of the test.

- If you're not sure what to do, ask your teacher.

Section A — Longer writing task

Bad Behaviour

Spend about 45 minutes on this section.

You are a pupil on the school council.

You receive this note from the head teacher:

I have been sent a letter by an elderly lady who lives near the school. She has complained about the behaviour of pupils leaving school each afternoon. She says they talk too loudly, kick footballs around and eat too many sweets.

I have already replied to her letter to explain that the pupils here are well behaved, but I think it would help if she received a letter from you as well. Please would you try to persuade her to come into school and see for herself that you and your friends are a well mannered and well behaved bunch?

You could also tell her about some of the things you and your friends do to contribute to the local community.

Write a letter to the elderly lady, persuading her that pupils at your school are well behaved and inviting her to visit so that she can see this for herself.

(30 marks)

Use this page to plan your work.

65

This page will not be marked.

- Why do you think pupils at your school are well behaved?

- What examples could you give of good behaviour?

- How do pupils at your school make a positive contribution to the local community?

- Why should the elderly lady visit your school?

Section B — Shorter writing task

Relaxation Area

Spend about 30 minutes on this section.

Your after-school youth club has received money to create a relaxation area and is running a competition to decide what it will be like.
The poster advertising the competition says:

> Have you got a winning idea?
>
> You're about to get a new relaxation area, but we need ideas for what it should be like.
>
> Tell us what you think we should put in this area and why. The best idea will become reality.

Write an entry for the competition, describing the new relaxation area you would like to see and why.

(20 marks including 4 for spelling)

Key Stage 3

English Test

Shakespeare Paper Romeo and Juliet

Set C

English

KEY STAGE 3

PRACTICE PAPER

Shakespeare

Set C

Read this page, but don't open the booklet until your teacher says you can start. Write your name and school in the spaces below.

First Name _____

Last Name _____

School _____

Instructions

- This test is **45 minutes** long.

- You will be tested on your reading and understanding of *Romeo and Juliet*. There are **18 marks** for this paper.

- Check through all of your work carefully before the end of the test.

- If you're not sure what to do, ask your teacher.

Romeo and Juliet
Act 1 Scene 1, lines 179 to 232
Act 2 Scene 2, lines 107 to 157

Imagine you are going to direct these extracts for a classroom performance.

In the first extract, Romeo tells Benvolio about Rosaline, a girl he loves.
In the second, Romeo and Juliet agree to get married.

How should the actor playing Romeo show his changing feelings about love in these extracts?

Support your ideas by referring to both of the extracts which are printed on the following pages.

(18 marks)

Romeo and Juliet
Act 1 Scene 1, lines 179 to 232

In this extract, Romeo talks to Benvolio about his feelings for Rosaline, a girl he is in love with.

ROMEO
Why, such is love's transgression.
Griefs of mine own lie heavy in my breast,   180
Which thou wilt propagate, to have it pressed
With more of thine; this love that thou hast shown
Doth add more grief to too much of mine own.
Love is a smoke made with the fume of sighs,
Being purged, a fire sparkling in lovers' eyes,   185
Being vexed a sea nourished with lovers' tears:
What is it else? A madness most discreet,
A choking gall and a preserving sweet.
Farewell, my coz.

BENVOLIO
                              Soft! I will go along;
And if you leave me so, you do me wrong.   190

ROMEO
Tut, I have lost myself; I am not here,
This is not Romeo, he's some other where.

BENVOLIO
Tell me in sadness, who is that you love.

ROMEO
What, shall I groan and tell thee?

BENVOLIO
                              Groan! Why no, —
But sadly tell me, who?   195

ROMEO
Bid a sick man in sadness make his will?
Ah, word ill urged to one that is so ill.
In sadness, cousin, I do love a woman.

BENVOLIO
I aimed so near, when I supposed you loved.

ROMEO
A right good mark-man! And she's fair I love.   200

BENVOLIO
A right fair mark, fair coz, is soonest hit.

ROMEO
Well, in that hit you miss: she'll not be hit
With Cupid's arrow, she hath Dian's wit;
And, in strong proof of chastity well armed,
From love's weak childish bow she lives uncharmed.   205
She will not stay the siege of loving terms,
Nor bide th'encounter of assailing eyes,
Nor ope her lap to saint-seducing gold:

	O, she is rich in beauty, only poor,	
	That when she dies with beauty dies her store.	210
BENVOLIO	Then she hath sworn that she will still live chaste?	
ROMEO	She hath, and in that sparing makes huge waste,	
	For beauty starved with her severity	
	Cuts beauty off from all posterity.	
	She is too fair, too wise, wisely too fair,	215
	To merit bliss by making me despair:	
	She hath forsworn to love, and in that vow	
	Do I live dead that live to tell it now.	
BENVOLIO	Be ruled by me, forget to think of her.	
ROMEO	O, teach me how I should forget to think.	220
BENVOLIO	By giving liberty unto thine eyes;	
	Examine other beauties.	
ROMEO	'Tis the way	
	To call hers, exquisite, in question more:	
	These happy masks that kiss fair ladies' brows,	
	Being black puts in mind they hide the fair;	225
	He that is strucken blind cannot forget	
	The precious treasure of his eyesight lost:	
	Show me a mistress that is passing fair,	
	What doth her beauty serve, but as a note	
	Where I may read who passed that passing fair?	230
	Farewell: thou canst not teach me to forget.	
BENVOLIO	I'll pay that doctrine, or else die in debt.	

Exeunt.

In this extract, Romeo is talking to Juliet at her balcony. They decide to get married the next day if they still feel so strongly about each other.

ROMEO   Lady, by yonder blessèd moon I vow,
            That tips with silver all these fruit-tree tops —

JULIET   O swear not by the moon, th'inconstant moon,
            That monthly changes in her circled orb,   110
            Lest that thy love prove likewise variable.

ROMEO   What shall I swear by?

JULIET   Do not swear at all.
            Or if thou wilt, swear by thy gracious self,
            Which is the god of my idolatry,
            And I'll believe thee.

ROMEO   If my heart's dear love —   115

JULIET   Well, do not swear. Although I joy in thee,
            I have no joy of this contract tonight,
            It is too rash, too unadvised, too sudden,
            Too like the lightning, which doth cease to be
            Ere one can say 'It lightens'. Sweet, good night.   120
            This bud of love, by summer's ripening breath,
            May prove a beauteous flower when next we meet.
            Good night, good night! as sweet repose and rest
            Come to thy heart as that within my breast.

ROMEO   O wilt thou leave me so unsatisfied?   125

JULIET   What satisfaction canst thou have tonight?

ROMEO   Th'exchange of thy love's faithful vow for mine.

JULIET   I gave thee mine before thou didst request it,
            And yet I would it were to give again.

ROMEO   Wouldst thou withdraw it? For what purpose, love?   130

JULIET   But to be frank and give it thee again,
            And yet I wish but for the thing I have.
            My bounty is as boundless as the sea,
            My love as deep; the more I give to thee
            The more I have, for both are infinite.   135

                    The NURSE is heard calling from inside.

I hear some noise within. Dear love, adieu! —
Anon, good Nurse! Sweet Montague, be true.
Stay but a little, I will come again.

Exit JULIET above

ROMEO	O blessèd, blessèd night! I am afeard,	
	Being in night, all this is but a dream,	140
	Too flattering-sweet to be substantial.	

Enter JULIET above

JULIET	Three words, dear Romeo, and good night indeed.	
	If that thy bent of love be honourable,	
	Thy purpose marriage, send me word tomorrow,	
	By one that I'll procure to come to thee,	145
	Where and what time thou wilt perform the rite,	
	And all my fortunes at thy foot I'll lay,	
	And follow thee my lord throughout the world.	

NURSE (*Calling from inside the house*)   Madam!

JULIET	I come, anon. But if thou meanest not well,	150
	I do beseech thee —	

NURSE (*Calling from inside the house*)   Madam!

JULIET	By and by I come —	
	To cease thy strife, and leave me to my grief.	
	Tomorrow will I send.	

ROMEO	So thrive my soul —

JULIET	A thousand times good night!

Exit JULIET above

ROMEO	A thousand times the worse, to want thy light.	155
	Love goes toward love as schoolboys from their books,	
	But love from love, toward school with heavy looks.	

END OF TEST

Key Stage 3

English Test

Shakespeare Paper
The Tempest
Set C

English

KEY STAGE
3

PRACTICE PAPER
Shakespeare
Set C

Read this page, but don't open the booklet until your teacher says you can start. Write your name and school in the spaces below.

First Name _____

Last Name _____

School _____

Instructions

- This test is **45 minutes** long.

- You will be tested on your reading and understanding of *The Tempest*. There are **18 marks** for this paper.

- Check through all of your work carefully before the end of the test.

- If you're not sure what to do, ask your teacher.

The Tempest

The Tempest
Act 1 Scene 2, lines 442 to 505
Act 3 Scene 1, lines 59 to 96

In the first extract, Ferdinand and Miranda fall in love and Prospero decides to test Ferdinand. In the second, Ferdinand and Miranda promise to marry each other.

How do these extracts explore the theme of one person having power over another?

Support your ideas by referring to both of the extracts which are printed on the following pages.

(18 marks)

The Tempest

Act 1 Scene 2, lines 442 to 505

In this extract, Miranda and Ferdinand begin to fall in love but Prospero wants to test their love for one another. He sets Ferdinand a test and makes him work for him. Miranda sticks up for Ferdinand even though Prospero tells her not to.

PROSPERO *(aside)*   The Duke of Milan
And his more braver daughter could control thee,
If now 'twere fit to do't. At the first sight
They have changed eyes. Delicate Ariel,   445
I'll set thee free for this. *(to* FERDINAND*)* A word, good sir —
I fear you have done yourself some wrong — a word.

MIRANDA *(aside)*   Why speaks my father so ungently? This
Is the third man that e'er I saw, the first
That e'er I sighed for. Pity move my father   450
To be inclined my way!

FERDINAND   O, if a virgin,
And your affection not gone forth, I'll make you
The Queen of Naples.

PROSPERO   Soft, sir, one word more!
(aside)   They are both in either's pow'rs, but this swift business
I must uneasy make, lest too light winning   455
Make the prize light. *(to* FERDINAND*)* One word more —
                                                            I charge thee
That thou attend me — thou dost here usurp
The name thou ow'st not and hast put thyself
Upon this island as a spy, to win it
From me, the lord on't.

FERDINAND   No, as I am a man.   460

MIRANDA   There's nothing ill can dwell in such a temple.
If the ill spirit have so fair a house,
Good things will strive to dwell with't.

PROSPERO   (to FERDINAND) Follow me.
(to MIRANDA) Speak not you for him — he's a traitor.
                                          (to FERDINAND) Come!
I'll manacle thy neck and feet together.   465
Sea-water shalt thou drink, thy food shall be
The fresh-brook mussels, withered roots, and husks
Wherein the acorn cradled. Follow.

FERDINAND   No —
I will resist such entertainment till
Mine enemy has more power.

He draws, and is charmed from moving.

MIRANDA	O dear father,	470
	Make not too rash a trial of him, for	
	He's gentle, and not fearful.	
PROSPERO	What, I say,	
	My foot my tutor? Put thy sword up, traitor,	
	Who mak'st a show but dar'st not strike, thy conscience	
	Is so possessed with guilt. Come from thy ward,	475
	For I can here disarm thee with this stick	
	And make thy weapon drop.	
MIRANDA	Beseech you, father!	
PROSPERO	Hence! Hang not on my garments.	
MIRANDA	Sir, have pity.	
	I'll be his surety.	
PROSPERO	Silence! One word more	
	Shall make me chide thee, if not hate thee. What!	480
	An advocate for an impostor! Hush!	
	Thou think'st there is no more such shapes as he,	
	Having seen but him and Caliban. Foolish wench!	
	To th' most of men this is a Caliban,	
	And they to him are angels.	
MIRANDA	My affections	485
	Are then most humble. I have no ambition	
	To see a goodlier man.	
PROSPERO	Come on — obey.	
	Thy nerves are in their infancy again,	
	And have no vigour in them.	
FERDINAND	So they are.	
	My spirits, as in a dream, are all bound up.	490
	My father's loss, the weakness which I feel,	
	The wreck of all my friends, nor this man's threats	
	To whom I am subdued, are but light to me,	
	Might I but through my prison once a day	
	Behold this maid. All corners else o' th' earth	495
	Let liberty make use of. Space enough	
	Have I in such a prison.	
PROSPERO (aside)	It works.	
	(to FERDINAND) Come on.	
	(to ARIEL) Thou hast done well, fine Ariel!	
	(to FERDINAND) Follow me.	
	(to ARIEL) Hark what thou else shalt do me.	
MIRANDA	(to FERDINAND) Be of comfort.	
	My father's of a better nature, sir,	500
	Than he appears by speech. This is unwonted	
	Which now came from him.	

PROSPERO *(to* ARIEL*)*   Thou shalt be as free
                              As mountain winds — but then exactly do
                              All points of my command.
ARIEL   To th' syllable.
PROSPERO *(to* FERDINAND*)* Come, follow. *(to* MIRANDA*)*
                                                        Speak not for him.   505

                              Exeunt.

Act 3 Scene 1, lines 59 to 96

In this extract, Ferdinand follows Prospero's orders and works hard
to prove his love for Miranda. Ferdinand and Miranda talk about their feelings for
one another and agree to get married. Prospero begins to see that their love is real.

FERDINAND   I am, in my condition,
                              A prince, Miranda. I do think, a king —   60
                              I would not so — and would no more endure
                              This wooden slavery than to suffer
                              The flesh-fly blow my mouth! Hear my soul speak:
                              The very instant that I saw you, did
                              My heart fly to your service, there resides   65
                              To make me slave to it, and for your sake
                              Am I this patient log-man.

MIRANDA   Do you love me?

FERDINAND   O heaven, O earth, bear witness to this sound,
                              And crown what I profess with kind event,
                              If I speak true! If hollowly, invert   70
                              What best is boded me to mischief! I,
                              Beyond all limit of what else i' th' world,
                              Do love, prize, honour you.

MIRANDA   I am a fool
                              To weep at what I am glad of.

PROSPERO *(Aside)*   Fair encounter
                              Of two most rare affections! Heavens rain grace   75
                              On that which breeds between 'em!

FERDINAND   Wherefore weep you?

MIRANDA   At mine unworthiness, that dare not offer

	What I desire to give, and much less take	
	What I shall die to want. But this is trifling,	
	And all the more it seeks to hide itself,	80
	The bigger bulk it shows. Hence, bashful cunning,	
	And prompt me, plain and holy innocence!	
	I am your wife, if you will marry me,	
	If not, I'll die your maid. To be your fellow	
	You may deny me, but I'll be your servant,	85
	Whether you will or no.	

FERDINAND   *(He kneels)*   My mistress, dearest,
And I thus humble ever.

MIRANDA   My husband, then?

FERDINAND   Ay, with a heart as willing
As bondage e'er of freedom. Here's my hand.

MIRANDA   And mine, with my heart in't. And now farewell   90
Till half an hour hence.

FERDINAND   A thousand thousand!

Exeunt FERDINAND *and* MIRANDA *separately*

PROSPERO   So glad of this as they I cannot be,
Who are surprised withal, but my rejoicing
At nothing can be more. I'll to my book,
For yet ere supper time must I perform   95
Much business appertaining.

Exit.

END OF TEST

Answers
How to Mark the Papers

It's pretty straightforward. You can mark all the papers using the mark schemes on the next few pages. Ask an adult to mark them for you if you like — it's good to get someone else's opinion of your work.

There are **lots** of good ways to answer every single one of the questions in these practice papers. That means we can't tell you **word for word** what your answer should be.

Instead we've given a description of the **kind** of answer that'll get you a certain number of marks. It might look a bit complicated, but once you get stuck in, it should all become clear.

Reading Paper

- Mark the **Reading** questions just for reading comprehension. Don't knock off marks for badly written answers, or give more marks for well written ones.

- Tot up the marks to get a score out of **32**.

Writing Paper

- This is marked for **sentence structure and punctuation**, **text structure and organisation** and **composition and effect**.

- Add up the separate marks for each task to get a mark out of **50**.

Shakespeare Paper

- The Shakespeare question is only marked for **understanding** — there are no marks for the written style.

- The Shakespeare question is marked out of **18**.

Using the Mark Schemes for the Writing Paper

- Read the work and then look at the **mark scheme tables** for each question. Decide which of the "What's the Answer Like?" descriptions matches it **most closely**.

- Each description gives a **range** of possible marks. If the answer does **every single thing** in one particular description, and does them well, give it a mark from the top end of the range. If the answer **doesn't** do everything in the description, but does do **some of it**, give it a mark from the bottom of the range.

- And obviously, the longest answers aren't necessarily the best ones.

Set A — Reading Paper

There are some really helpful points about marking
on page 79— make sure you read them first.

1. 1 mark for an answer which gives all three abilities:
   - fly
   - drink blood
   - run / sprint

2. 1 mark for any valid explanation, e.g.
   - He uses an exclamation mark to make it sound like something dramatic has happened.
   - He uses a slang word "Yikes" to amuse us and encourage us to think we'll understand the article.

3. 2 marks for a clear explanation, including a quotation, e.g.
   - He starts paragraph 6 with the phrase "Thing is," which expresses a reservation about what has gone before.
   - He repeats the words "small animals," which shows that the two paragraphs have a subject in common.

4a. 1 mark for a valid phrase, e.g.
   - "fleet-footed"
   - "sprint along the ground"
   - "break into a loping run"

4b. 1 mark for the word "lumbering"

5. A good answer is likely to cover points like the high number of quotes, use of comparisons (e.g. "flop around like fish out of water" or "It's as if they were designed to chase race cars…"), mixing of scientific quotes with simple explanations (e.g. "You might want to jog across the room… to understand what that means") and the way subheadings identify section topics.

   1 or 2 marks for an explanation that recognises that the tone is light-hearted and picks out some examples but does not cover all three prompts.

   3 marks for an explanation that comments on the effects of specific details and quotations but does not cover all three prompts in detail.

   4 or 5 marks for a detailed answer in which all three prompts are dealt with and comments are supported with appropriate quotations and explanations.

6. 1 mark for a valid answer, e.g.
   - He writes as though he is talking directly to the reader in chatty, informal language.
   - He uses multiple exclamation marks to show excitement about the topic.
   - He describes a grotesque and humorous scene from a film.

7. 1 mark for a valid answer, e.g.
   - The book explores important themes (such as family, friendship, making sacrifices).

8. 1 mark for the point that it should contain shocking, thrilling, action-packed, violent events.

   1 mark for the point that it should contain more subtle moments that make the reader think and brood.

9. A good explanation might cover the enduring nature of his enthusiasm e.g. "That thirst for 'more' has never left me"; the range and type of emotions triggered by horror stories, e.g. it "explores" themes, "lingers" in the mind and contrasts "the subtle menace between the sudden bursts of action and violence"; the effect of single and multiple exclamation marks, and the unsettling effect of ellipses ("...") in paragraph 5.

   1 or 2 marks for general comments which recognise Shan's enjoyment of reading and writing horror. There will be some reference to the text but some of the prompts may not be covered.

   3 marks for an answer that comments on the effects of specific details and quotations. Some of the prompts may not be covered in detail.

   4 or 5 marks for a detailed answer in which all three prompts are dealt with and comments are supported with appropriate quotations and explanations.

10. 1 mark for a valid answer, e.g.
   - He saw everything by "moonlight."
   - "a breath of fresh air, though it were of the night" — he is describing night air.
   - "this nocturnal existence" — he is making it clear that he only moves around at night.

11. 1 mark for each row completed, to a maximum of 2 marks. **Must include a valid quotation** and an explanation e.g.
   - "I felt that I was indeed in prison" — He feels trapped.
   - "It is destroying my nerve" — He is starting to get jumpy and scared.
   - "there is ground for my terrible fear in this accursed place" — He is convinced that the castle is dangerous.

Set A — Reading Paper

There are some really helpful points about marking on page 79— make sure you read them first.

12a. 1 mark for a valid description of a feeling and 1 mark for a supporting quotation, e.g. he's beginning to relax as he looks at the beautiful landscape — "there was peace and comfort in every breath I drew."

12b. 1 mark for a valid description of a feeling and 1 mark for a supporting quotation, e.g. he is disgusted and frightened by the strange sight of the Count — "my very feelings changed to repulsion and terror".

13. 1 mark for a valid answer — must include an example with an explanation, e.g.

- "I am in fear, in awful fear" — repeating the word fear emphasises how extreme his emotion is.

- "What manner of man is this, or what manner of creature" — repeating the word "manner" shows how uncertain he is about the creature he can see.

14. 1 mark for each valid explanation in the "Effect on the reader" column, up to a maximum of 4 marks, e.g.

For *"Hopping is good…roll over and squash a bat"*

- "slurping" makes the bat sound comical.

- The idea of it being squashed makes it seem more vulnerable.

For *"the clever little mammals…"*

- The phrase "little mammals" makes them sound endearing.

- Calling them "clever little mammals" suggests that we could admire the bats, not fear them.

For *"down the castle wall…like great wings"*

- The description of the Count above the "dreadful abyss" makes him sound confident and frightening.

- The words "like great wings" emphasise his power and strangeness.

For *"what manner of creature is it…"*

- Imprecise words like "manner" and "semblance" create a feeling of mystery about who or what the Count is.

- The use of a question helps emphasise the narrator's confusion to the reader.

Set B — Reading Paper

There are some really helpful points about marking
on page 79— make sure you read them first.

1. 1 mark for any valid answer e.g.

    • It was because things kept moving around, e.g. the people in the portraits.

2a. 1 mark for any one of the following phrases:

    • "He would drop waste-paper baskets on your head"

    • "pull rugs from under your feet"

    • "pelt you with bits of chalk"

    • "sneak up behind you, invisible, grab your nose"

2b. 1 mark for a reasonable explanation e.g.

    • The list shows he's unpleasant in many ways.

    • The list emphasises how unpleasant he is.

3. 1 mark for a valid example e.g.

    • Doors that won't open unless you ask them politely or tickle them in the right place.

    • The poltergeist Peeves drops waste-paper baskets on people's heads.

    1 mark for a valid explanation e.g.

    • The humour is quirky and surprising.

    • The description has a slapstick humour, like a cartoon.

4. Ideas for answering this question include the writer's use of descriptive language, her matter-of-fact telling of magical events and the way her characters have adapted to them in practical ways.

    1 or 2 marks for a simple answer that attempts to answer the question but doesn't cover all three of the prompts.

    3 marks for an answer that covers all three prompts but isn't developed.

    4 or 5 marks for an answer that covers all three prompts, is clear and detailed and has points supported with quotations.

5. 1 mark for any valid technique, e.g.

    • first paragraph is printed in bold

    • short sentences

    • repetition

    • emotive language

    1 mark for a valid explanation, e.g.

    • Short sentences stop the reader from becoming bored.

    • Repetition makes the reader curious about what is coming next.

    • Emotive language makes the reader care about what is happening.

6. 1 mark for a valid impression, 1 further mark for a supporting quotation, e.g.

    • It's imposing — "the grand double door".

    • It's got lots of facilities — "there is a work room, kitchen, common room and the sofa room."

7. 1 mark for each row of the table completed with a valid description of how that aspect of the article helps the reader.

    Example answers for "Sections describing different pupils' experiences":

    • They show the reader different points of view.

    • They help the reader remember what it felt like to start a new school.

    Example answers for "Headline and subheadings":

    • They make it clear what the article and different sections are about.

    • They divide the article up so that it isn't so daunting.

8. Answers for this question could comment on the excitement expressed by all three students, the use of direct questions in the introduction to make the reader think about their own experience and the use of the headmaster's comment to make general rather than specific statements.

    1 or 2 marks for a simple answer that attempts to address some but not all of the prompts.

    3 marks for an answer that attempts to address all three prompts but isn't detailed or doesn't use quotations to support ideas.

    4 or 5 marks for an answer that clearly addresses all three prompts and answers the question using quotations or examples from the text.

9. 1 mark for a valid comment e.g.

    • It seemed tough but happy.

    • It sounds unpleasant and difficult.

    1 further mark for a relevant supporting quotation e.g.

    • "Despite these conditions, Cherry-Anne and Lisbeth have happy memories..."

    • "The schoolroom was crowded, dark and cold".

10. 1 mark for any valid example, e.g.

    • The boys "were each given one stroke with the cane on the hand".

Set B — Reading Paper

There are some really helpful points about marking on page 79 — make sure you read them first.

11. 1 mark for any reasonable suggestion, e.g.

- The logbook entries make the story more interesting.
- The logbook entries help us understand the day-to-day running of the school more clearly.

12. 1 mark for each valid quotation and explanation, up to a maximum of 3 marks, e.g.

- "hanging war issue blankets from the ceiling" — gives the reader the idea that materials were basic and that the school staff were doing their best with limited resources.
- "did little to stop the noise" — emphasises to the reader how cramped the conditions were.
- "stop the heat from ... reaching the far end" — makes the reader feel sorry for the children.
- "had to wear her outdoor coat all day to keep warm" — makes the reader empathise with Lisbeth by describing how she coped with the difficult conditions.

13. 1 mark for an appropriate choice for the purpose of the text, and 1 mark for a valid explanation. Up to a maximum of 4 marks, e.g.

	Wingrave School	Harry Potter and the Philosopher's Stone
Purpose of the text (circle your answer)	entertaining ⟨informing⟩ persuading	⟨entertaining⟩ informing persuading
Give a reason for your choice	The text uses lots of factual, real-life detail about evacuation, e.g. the number of children evacuated from Tufnell Park in London.	The text uses entertaining humour to describe the school, e.g. portraits that keep going to visit each other.

Set C — Reading Paper

*There are some really helpful points about marking
on page 79 — make sure you read them first.*

1. 1 mark for any valid phrase, e.g.
   - "Let there be none to mark"
   - "Rest in the woodland free"
   - "the loveliness bold / Loneliest landscapes wear"

2. 1 mark for each simile, up to a maximum of 2 marks:
   - "Bright as the heavens above"
   - "Fresh as the wild bush flowers"

3. a) 1 mark: "Give us"

   b) 1 mark for any reasonable explanation, e.g.
   - It links the first three verses.
   - It makes the poem sound like a prayer.
   - It makes the reader feel like part of the poem.

4. 1 or 2 marks for an explanation which: picks out some relevant examples in response to the prompts; does **not** cover all three prompts; makes very simple comments in response to the prompts; does not explicitly tackle the question of how the poet builds up a picture of the bush.

   3 marks for an explanation which: picks out and explains examples relevant to all three prompts, giving a basic overview of how the poet builds up a picture of the bush.

   4 or 5 marks for an explanation which: explicitly explores how the writer creates a picture of the bush; picks out and explains examples of all three prompts.

5. 1 mark for any valid phrase, e.g.
   - "biggest challenge of my life so far"
   - "no-one would turn their back on this chance"

6. 1 mark for any valid phrase up to a maximum of 1 mark, e.g.
   - steep landscape
   - land flattened out
   - grey flint lake
   - greenery was sparse.

7. 1 mark for each explanation **backed up with a quotation** up to a maximum of 3 marks, e.g.
   - contrast between the rock climb and the "relative comfort of the lake side"
   - emphasising how hard it is with phrases like "it wasn't possible to make out any kind of route"
   - short sentences like "The ropes were uncoiled and the harness was on"
   - explaining how vulnerable she felt with phrases like "it might not stop me being injured in a serious fall"

8. ½ mark for each factual answer drawn from the text, up to a maximum of 2 marks, e.g.
   - You can attach the rope to the top of the cliff for short climbs.
   - Make sure ropes are clean and dry when put away.
   - Coil ropes carefully.
   - You climb in pairs.

9. 1 or 2 marks for an explanation which: picks out some relevant examples in response to the prompts; does **not** cover all three prompts; makes very simple comments in response to the prompts, which do not engage with the climber's experience.

   3 marks for an explanation which: picks out and explains examples relevant to all three prompts, giving a basic overview of how the writer conveys her feelings to the reader.

   4 or 5 marks for an explanation which: explicitly explores how the writer conveys her feelings to the reader; picks out and explains examples of all three prompts.

10. ½ mark for each appropriate word/phrase up to a maximum of 1 mark, e.g.
    - "the speediest" • "sexiest" • "snatched"
    - "hot off his wheels" • "under the handlebars".

Set C — Reading Paper

*There are some really helpful points about marking
on page 79— make sure you read them first.*

11. 1 mark for each relevant quotation **with explanation** (maximum 2 marks), e.g.

- "I didn't really think about it on the way round" — shows he is committed to racing and concentrates hard when riding.
- "I just had to focus on getting round" — shows concentration.
- "I think you've got to be ready to ride in anything" shows commitment whatever the weather.
- "You should be training in all weathers" shows he is prepared to put in the hard work.

12. 1 mark for each quotation **with explanation** that answers the question (maximum 2 marks), e.g.

- "I knew I was making good time" — shows Andrew is confident.
- "it's easy to blame the mud" — he doesn't think much of people who make excuses.
- "you've got to be ready to ride in anything" — shows Andrew is tough and dedicated.

13. 1 mark for any valid answer, e.g.

- Andrew pestered his parents
- His dad was keen on bikes
- His parents knew he was serious about it

14. 1 mark for any valid **similarity**, e.g.

- The texts are both about people dedicated to their activity.
- Both texts describe the excitement people find in challenging situations.

1 mark for a valid explanation of **how this feature affects the reader**, e.g.

- It encourages the reader to respect / admire the people described.
- It helps the reader understand how people who do extreme sports feel about what they do.

1 mark for any valid **difference**, e.g.

- *Going Up* goes into a lot more detail about how the writer feels. Uses more descriptive and emotive language. The *Mountain Bike Champion* interview is chattier and focuses more on the physical side of the sport.
- *Going Up* is from the point of view of a beginner, but *Mountain Bike Champion* tells you the views of someone who has won a medal and is very experienced.

1 mark for any valid explanation of **how the difference affects the reader**, e.g.

- *Going Up* makes the reader feel more personally involved. It is more exciting to read because it talks about the climb, and the climber's feelings as she did it, in detail. *Mountain Bike Champion* doesn't discuss the biker's feelings in much detail.
- You get very different perspectives on extreme sports from the two articles. The beginner who is slightly scared in *Going Up* has a different perspective to the experienced biker in *Mountain Bike Champion*.

Writing Paper — Section A — Sets A, B & C

*There are some really helpful points about marking
on page 79— make sure you read them first.*

> You can use the same mark scheme to mark any of the Section A questions for
> **Sentence Structure and Punctuation** and **Text Structure and Organisation**
> (see below and on the next page). To mark questions for **Composition and Effect**,
> find the correct mark scheme for the specific question on pages 88-90.

Sentence Structure and Punctuation

WHAT'S THE ANSWER LIKE?	MARK
• Only makes use of simple connectives such as "and" / "but". • Noun phrases short and simple, e.g. "narrow streets". • Little or no use of pronouns and few attempts to vary vocabulary. • Little or no variation in punctuation — uses full stops and commas.	**0** marks
• Uses some more varied connectives to link parts of sentences, e.g. "although" or "because". • Some noun phrases expanded, but in a simple way, e.g. "narrow and winding streets". • Makes some attempts to use subordinate clauses, e.g. "Harry wasn't sure what to do next, so he sat down on a park bench to think about it." • Mostly simple verbs used in the present tense. • Attempts to use a range of punctuation, although this may be limited.	**1-2** marks
• Connectives more varied and used more confidently, sometimes developing a sentence beyond simple clause and subordinate clause, e.g. "Although Harry wasn't exactly sure what he should do with the money, he did know that he was going to enjoy spending every single penny…" • Uses expanding noun phrases such as "The narrow, winding streets at the centre of town are very old, possibly medieval…" • Some attempt to vary sentence starters, such as "If I were you" / "Maybe you shouldn't". • Punctuation mostly used correctly, and some variety shown, e.g. exclamation marks, brackets.	**3-4** marks
• Good use of a range of connectives such as "on the other hand" / "however". • Sentence length and type varied for effect, e.g. includes impersonal sentences like "It is important that..." • Good use of a wide range of punctuation.	**5-6** marks
• Good range of sentence starters, such as "On the other hand…" / "Some people think…" • Uses a good range of sentence constructions, varying length of clause / subclause for effect. • Can write in an impersonal tone to increase impact of text, e.g. "Many people say that…" • Makes use of a wide range of punctuation to good effect.	**7** marks
• Secure and confident control of sentences and their structure for maximum effect. • Uses a wide range of sentence constructions, e.g. rhetorical questions, complex sentences, concise sentences. • Uses the full range of punctuation effectively.	**8** marks

Now look at the next page and mark the piece for "Text Structure and Organisation"…

Writing Paper — Section A — Sets A, B & C

*There are some really helpful points about marking
on page 79— make sure you read them first.*

Text Structure and Organisation

WHAT'S THE ANSWER LIKE?	MARK
• Very limited introduction or conclusion. • Very little structure, e.g. few or no paragraphs. • Some simple linking of ideas, e.g. "and then" / "also".	**0** marks
• Some clear attempt at a beginning, middle and end. • Some use of paragraphs to divide main groups of ideas. • Topic sentences used to introduce some paragraphs, e.g. "In the city centre there is a lot more to do…" • Some topic sentences developed into further ideas, but in a limited way.	**1-2** marks
• New ideas divided into paragraphs. • Some attempt to follow a structure, e.g. "You say you're thinking about running away… but I can't believe…" • Some more varied connectives used, such as "however" / "although". • Some development of ideas within paragraphs by giving examples or more detail.	**3-4** marks
• Paragraphs consistently linked with more complicated connectives such as "In addition to the leisure centre…" / "Finally, having finished the tennis match…" • Paragraphs introduced with a strong starter sentence, e.g. "The importance of comprehensive leisure facilities cannot be overstated." • Ideas within paragraphs more fully developed, e.g. by using supporting evidence.	**5-6** marks
• Paragraphs are all well organised to make the text clear and effective. • Connectives consistently and effectively used to develop points or arguments. • Discourse markers used to show stage of argument or piece, e.g. "At last…" or "Firstly, Alex…" • Variety of well thought out sentence structures within a paragraph, that flow effectively.	**7** marks
• Suitable number of paragraphs of a suitable length to constitute a clear argument. • Each paragraph follows the previous one smoothly and logically. • Complex topic sentences direct readers' attention to argument / ideas. • Paragraph content and structure consistently, carefully and confidently controlled for maximum effect.	**8** marks

*Now look at pages 88-90, and mark the piece for "Composition and Effect".
There are different mark schemes for each paper...*

Writing Paper — Section A — Set A

*There are some really helpful points about marking
on page 79— make sure you read them first.*

Composition and Effect — Set A, Improving the Common Room

WHAT'S THE ANSWER LIKE?	MARK
• Little understanding of audience or purpose of the text. • Brief piece of writing with little detail and no developed ideas. • No attempt to explain the decisions.	**0** marks
• Attempts to organise ideas into paragraphs. • Some clear information on what has been done. • Gives some reasons for spending choices.	**1-3** marks
• Good opening paragraph which makes intentions clear. • Detailed information about several decisions with some reasons mentioned. • Appropriate choice of formal language.	**4-6** marks
• Report is well organised into distinct sections. • Describes details of spending with convincing reasons. • Clear sense of how students have benefited. • Consistent and appropriate formal tone.	**7-9** marks
• Clearly organised paragraphs which cover a variety of information. • Well-developed explanations of a range of decisions and outcomes. • Several benefits explained. • Good use of varied formal language appropriate to the audience.	**10-12** marks
• Report is well organised, with an easy-to-follow structure. • Interesting and realistic range of improvements and benefits mentioned. • Each decision / benefit is fully and clearly explained. • Confident, convincing formal tone conveys appreciation for the Parents' Association's help.	**13-14** marks

Writing Paper — Section A — Set B

*There are some really helpful points about marking
on page 79— make sure you read them first.*

Composition and Effect — Set B, Teen Readers

What's the Answer Like?	Mark
• Little understanding of the audience or the purpose of the task. • Brief piece of writing with few details or ideas. • No attempt to use the conventions of a report.	**0** marks
• Some attempt to tackle the purpose of the writing. • Some awareness that the report should be formal. • Some details about why teenagers might not like the library and / or how they could be encouraged to use it more.	**1-3** marks
• Fairly good opening paragraph that shows awareness of the purpose of the report. • Some good use of formal language appropriate for the purpose, e.g. "In my opinion" • Some points developed well with more detail and information, e.g. "Furthermore, Smithtown library has seen numbers rise because..." • Offers some evidence to support ideas, such as made-up quotations from teenagers.	**4-6** marks
• Clearly addresses audience and purpose of task. • Uses a consistently appropriate tone for advising, e.g. "I really believe that if we offer this we will see more teenagers coming through our doors". • Consistent use of formal language appropriate to a report for a boss. • Several detailed points and ideas with developed supporting evidence. • Clearly organised into paragraphs or sections.	**7-9** marks
• Convincing report which fulfils its objectives. • Well organised into paragraphs that follow on logically and clearly from one another, e.g. using signposts such as "In addition to these points..." • Makes confident and varied use of supporting evidence such as made-up quotations, personal stories or statistics. • Tone, style and language are appropriate and effective throughout.	**10-12** marks
• Well organised, realistic and easy-to-follow report which fulfils its objectives. • All points fully developed with a variety of supporting evidence used when appropriate. • Convincing and successful use of formal tone throughout. • Varied and interesting use of formal language appropriate for advising a boss.	**13-14** marks

Writing Paper — Section A — Set C

*There are some really helpful points about marking
on page 79— make sure you read them first.*

Composition and Effect — Set C, Bad Behaviour

WHAT'S THE ANSWER LIKE?	MARK
• Little understanding of the audience or the purpose of the text. • Little written with few details or ideas shown. • No attempt to use conventions of a formal letter.	**0** marks
• Attempts to tackle the purpose of the writing. • Some awareness that the letter should be formal, e.g. "I understand that you have written to our head teacher..." • Some examples of persuasive writing, such as "I'm sure you agree..."	**1-3** marks
• Good opening paragraph that sets out the purpose of the letter. • Fairly good use of formal language. Not always consistent. • Some points developed well with more detail and information, e.g. "One example of the things we do for the local community is providing entertainment at the local old people's home..." • Some awareness of appropriate tone to persuade an older person.	**4-6** marks
• Clearly addresses audience and purpose of task. • Appropriate tone. • Consistent use of formal language that is respectful to the elderly lady. • Some detailed points and ideas with developed supporting evidence. • Clearly organised into paragraphs.	**7-9** marks
• Persuasive and realistic letter. • Well organised into paragraphs that follow on logically and clearly from one another, using signposts such as "Consequently..." or "However..." • Points supported by varied and persuasive evidence. • Tone, style and language appropriate and effective throughout.	**10-12** marks
• Effective, realistic and easy-to-follow letter. • Fully developed, interesting points supported with detailed evidence. • Persuasive but respectful tone throughout. • Varied and interesting use of formal language appropriate for a letter.	**13-14** marks

Writing Paper — Section B — Sets A, B & C

There are some really helpful points about marking
on page 79 — make sure you read them first.

You can use the same mark scheme to mark any of the Section B questions for **Spelling** and **Sentence Structure, Punctuation and Text Organisation**. To mark questions for **Composition and Effect**, find the correct mark scheme for the specific question on pages 92-93.

Spelling

WHAT'S THE ANSWER LIKE?	MARK
• Simple words of one syllable spelt correctly. • Common words of more than one syllable spelt correctly, e.g. because. • Some words confused, e.g. here / hear. • Some words spelt as they sound, e.g. secondry instead of secondary.	**1** mark
• Most words that follow a regular pattern spelt correctly. • Some more difficult words spelt incorrectly, e.g. rec<u>ie</u>ve instead of rec<u>ei</u>ve. • Some prefixes and suffixes spelt incorrectly, e.g. di<u>ss</u>appeared instead of di<u>s</u>appeared.	**2** marks
• Most words spelt correctly, including unusual words. • Some minor mistakes such as unstressed vowels missed out, e.g. diffrent instead of different. • Occasional mistakes with more difficult words.	**3** marks
• Almost every word spelt perfectly. • Any very minor slips are rare and not repeated.	**4** marks

Sentence Structure, Punctuation and Text Organisation

WHAT'S THE ANSWER LIKE?	MARK
• Makes use of only very simple connectives, such as "and". • Makes no use of pronouns (e.g. he, she, it). • Most sentences constructed correctly, but basic. • Makes little or no use of punctuation beyond full stops and commas.	**0** marks
• Sometimes uses simple subordinate clauses to extend sentences, e.g. "<u>Though you may get slightly uncomfortable</u>, all the money we raise will go to a good charitable cause." • Makes use of modal verbs, like "might", "may", "could" etc. • Beginning to use more complex sentences. • Sentences grouped together with the same topic. • More varied use of punctuation, but still limited.	**1-2** marks
• Longer and more complex sentences including some with several parts. • Makes use of more complex verb forms, e.g. imperatives such as "Beware!" • Sentences organised into paragraphs. • Points developed within paragraphs. • Punctuation used correctly and with some variety.	**3-4** marks
• Sustained use of complex sentences. • Sentence length and style varied for effect. • Range of connectives used effectively and confidently, both in sentences and between paragraphs — e.g. "You will need to perform for 15 minutes, <u>so</u> make sure you have enough material." • Paragraphs clearly organised and flow smoothly. • Variety of punctuation used confidently and successfully.	**5** marks
• Able to use a range of verb forms consistently and successfully, including the passive voice to maintain an impersonal tone, where appropriate — e.g. "the changes <u>were well received</u>." • Points clearly and thoroughly developed. • Topic sentences used to begin paragraphs and paragraphs organised carefully for maximum effect. • Confident use of varied punctuation to good effect.	**6** marks

Writing Paper — Section B — Set A

*There are some really helpful points about marking
on page 79— make sure you read them first.*

Composition and Effect — Set A, Summer Fair Fundraising

What's the Answer Like?	Mark
• Little or no awareness of audience or purpose of text. • No use made of information in the prompt. • No attempt to engage interest through choice of language.	**0** marks
• Some awareness of writing for teaching staff. • Attempts to give reasons why they should volunteer. • A few attempts to sound persuasive, e.g. "You ought to volunteer"; "We need you to volunteer"; "It will be good".	**1-3** marks
• Sounds quite convincing with friendly but polite tone. • Several reasons for volunteering are given. • Vocabulary varied for persuasive effect, e.g. "this rare opportunity"; "star in the summer fair spectacular".	**4-6** marks
• Tone is light-hearted but still formal enough for staff audience. • A good range of convincing reasons to volunteer given. • Several persuasive devices used, e.g. rhetorical questions, examples, sets of three, statistics, emotive language.	**7-9** marks
• Well controlled tone of friendly persuasion, humour and the appropriate level of formality. • Intelligent use made of information in the prompt. • Uses a wide range of persuasive devices, e.g. anticipating staff response with counter-argument such as "You'll probably get wet but the water is nice and warm." • Well argued piece of writing which flows and is easy to read.	**10** marks

Writing Paper — Section B — Sets B&C

Composition and Effect — Set B, Talent Contest

WHAT'S THE ANSWER LIKE?	MARK
• Little awareness shown of audience or purpose of text. • No attempt to address points suggested in the task. • Little written and little to attract readers' interest.	**0** marks
• Some awareness shown of the task's audience and purpose. • Some attempts to offer simple information relating to the talent contest. • Some use of effective vocabulary and some simple noun phrases, e.g. "The talent show will be an exciting competition."	**1-3** marks
• Good awareness of the task's audience and purpose. • Uses a range of devices to inform the audience about the talent contest and keep them interested. • Covers the ideas suggested in the task, with some developed in more detail.	**4-6** marks
• Makes an effort to catch the audience's attention from the beginning. • Well organised and informative writing. • Good use of devices, such as subheadings, to interest and inform the reader. • Appropriate use of informal language.	**7-9** marks
• Convincing and realistic leaflet that is appropriate for its audience and purpose. • Well organised and easy to follow, with varied and helpful stylistic devices. • Detailed and well developed points. • Confidently written.	**10** marks

Composition and Effect — Set C, Relaxation Area

WHAT'S THE ANSWER LIKE?	MARK
• Little or no awareness of audience or purpose of text. • No attempt to provide the information requested in the task. • Little written and little attempt to describe a new relaxation area.	**0** marks
• Some awareness shown of task's audience and purpose. • Some attempts to describe the relaxation area, but little detail. • Some simple noun phrases such as, "The room should have comfortable seats. The room should have music playing in it."	**1-3** marks
• Some good awareness of the task's audience and purpose. • Suggested ideas are tackled more thoroughly, for example, "I'd like to see lilac walls with some artwork dotted around." • Uses varied language and descriptive devices. • Covers fully the requested information with some developed information where appropriate.	**4-6** marks
• Good awareness of the task's audience and purpose. • Interesting and descriptive piece of writing. • Varied use of devices such as rhetorical questions, emotive language and detail to interest the reader. • Sentences fully developed.	**7-9** marks
• Enjoyable and convincing descriptive writing, suitable for its audience and purpose. • Lots of original descriptive detail that avoids cliché. • Well organised, varied and imaginative. • Developed in an appropriate and well-controlled way.	**10** marks

Shakespeare Papers

There are some really helpful points about marking on page 79 — make sure you read them first.

1) Count up the number of separate points made to answer the essay question.
   On the appropriate grid, tick one box for each point (up to 6 ticks).

2) Tick one box for every one of those points that's backed up by a quote (up to 6 ticks).

3) Then tick one box for every point that's expanded with a comment (up to 6 ticks).

4) Finally count up all the ticks to give a mark out of 18.

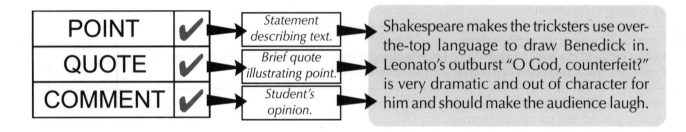

POINT	✔	→	Statement describing text.	→	Shakespeare makes the tricksters use over-the-top language to draw Benedick in. Leonato's outburst "O God, counterfeit?" is very dramatic and out of character for him and should make the audience laugh.
QUOTE	✔	→	Brief quote illustrating point.	→	
COMMENT	✔	→	Student's opinion.	→	

Set A — Shakespeare Paper

POINT	✔					
QUOTE						
COMMENT						

Set B — Shakespeare Paper

POINT	✔					
QUOTE						
COMMENT						

Set C — Shakespeare Paper

POINT	✔					
QUOTE						
COMMENT						

EHB33